SNAP SHOT™

Art director Roger Priddy
Editor Mary Ling
Designer Claire Penny

A Dorling Kindersley Book

First published in Great Britain in
1994 by Snapshot™, an imprint of
Covent Garden Books
9 Henrietta Street, London, WC2E 8PS

A CIP catalogue record for this book is
available from the British Library
ISBN 1-85948-010-1
Colour reproduction by Colourscan
Printed in Belgium by Proost

Animal
Antics

Contents

Playful puppies

5

Is anyone there?

A tiny mouse peeps out, checking there are no hungry cats about. Now it can scurry off to find some food.

What a bunny tunnel!

This little rabbit has discovered a
tunnel it might make its home. But
its burrow has more room for friends!

Who are you?

This little kitten is scared of cuddly toys, so it fluffs up its fur to look bigger.

Do chimps chat?

Chimps can be very noisy when they talk. They screech, scream, growl and howl.

These hairy friends
are hooting hello
to each other.

What a busy day!

Four sleepy kittens have had a long day
play-fighting and pouncing on leaves.

These games will teach the kittens how to be grown-up cats.

13

Shall we play ball?

Sea-lions have big flippers, webbed feet and sleek bodies to help them speed through water. They also love playing games.

Are you tired, chicks?

These crafty chicks often climb onto mum's back when they are tired and fall asleep among her soft feathers.

Who is behind you?

A budgerigar thinks its rabbit friend makes a good perch. Or maybe the rabbit has an itch it can't reach.

Who is a greedy pig?

This hungry pig is looking for food. Instead it finds that its head is too big for the bucket.

Penguin pals

Two fuzzy king penguin chicks are keeping each other warm while the grown-ups go fishing.

Going for a dip, ducks?

These yellow ducklings have just hatched. They are waddling off for their first swim.

Unlucky puppy!

All puppies have secret places to hide snacks. Maybe this puppy has forgotten where it buried its biscuit.

Does it taste good?

This puppy is having a good gnaw on an old shoe. Chewing helps its new sharp teeth to grow through.

Can you jump like me?

With its powerful springy legs and sticky tongue the tree-frog is the fastest fly-catcher in the forest!

What can a toucan do?

A toucan can use its large beak to snap off nuts and berries from branches.

How shall we stay warm

This squirrel and kitten have been friends since birth. They are always playing together. In the winter

in the winter?

their thick coats keep out the cold. But the squirrel is even warmer with a kitten as a furry pillow!

Bonkers
for bananas?

The orang-
utan is the swing
king. Its long arms
are perfect for
swooping through
the trees to pick fruit.

Squawking for supper?

A raised plume and loud squawks from the cockatoo warns you to keep back, or be pecked!

Who is that kitten

Kittens are very curious,
and love exploring. This adventurous
kitten has just met its match. "Haven't
I seen this kitten before?"

in there?